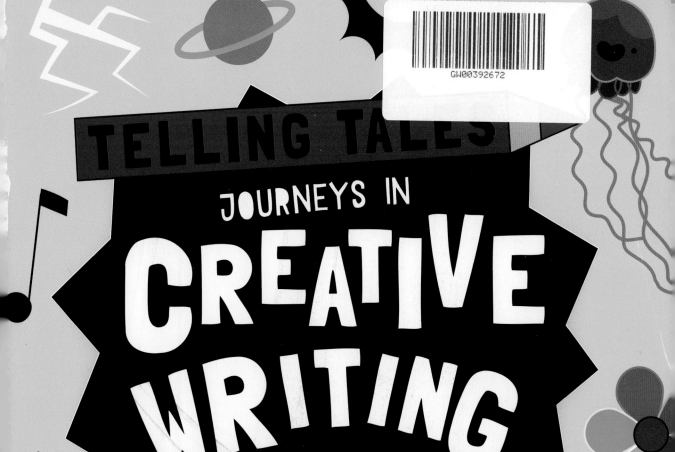

TELLING TALES

JOURNEYS IN
CREATIVE WRITING

Written by Rudi Haig

Illustrations by Kim Hankinson

b small

Published by b small publishing ltd. www.bsmall.co.uk © b small publishing ltd. 2022   1 2 3 4 5   ISBN 978-1-913918-45-3
Publisher: Sam Hutchinson   Art director: Vicky Barker   Printed in China by WKT Co. Ltd.

Proper introductions

Hello, I'm Ms. Adjective the Adventurer. It's great to finally meet you. I will be your guide in the weird and wonderful World of Creative Writing. I'm excited to show you all the strange and stupendous places we're about to explore but please be warned: there are unexpected pitfalls ahead!

I was about your age when I first came here but little did I realise then, that you need to use your creativity to progress through this world. So come with me and let's use words and language to shape our imaginations and complete tricky tasks so you can get home safely.

Adventure HQ

Getting to know each other ...

We need to choose a companion to accompany us on our trip but first, let's get to know each other a little better.

Please answer the following questions. You don't need to write these down, just say them out loud. I'll be able to hear you.

1. What's your favourite colour?

2. Where do you live?

3. What's your favourite food?

Here are my answers:

1. Red – it's the colour of apples, my favourite fruit, and my parrot Squawk.

2. I live here in Adventure Headquarters in The World of Creative Writing.

3. Pizza – I love how crunchy, chewy and salty it is. Yum!

Keep an eye out for:

FAB FIVER!

'Fab Fivers'
five useful words
or phrases.

'ADVENTURE CLUES'
these are tips and
trivia that you pick
up along the way.

Choosing our companion

Are you looking forward to our big journey? Not long now. In my experience, it's better to have at least three adventurers travel together. So we can bring more supplies with us and have more fun sharing the experience with others. But who shall we bring?

All four of my pets want to come. There's Scaredy the tortoise, Squawk the parrot, Fluffy the dog and Meow the cat.

Adventure HQ

FAB FIVER!

Meow

Squawk

Buzz

Whoosh

Slap

ADVENTURE CLUE:
'Supplies' are things needed for living or surviving, like water and food.

The decision

- Squawk hurt his wing crashing into the sofa and needs to rest up at Adventure HQ.
- Meow is an indoor cat, so she won't be happy going outside.
- Scaredy is actually very brave but might struggle to keep up with our pace.
- Fluffy is a little naughty but fit and fast ... so he's coming with us!

Who from your life would you have chosen to join us? Is it a friend, pet or family member? Write down your choice, mentioning two things about them that would make them great members of our team.

How cliché! I'm pretty fast, thank you very much!

Picking up provisions

OK, one last thing: provisions. What do you need to bring? I've got all sorts of bits and pieces including maps and a juicy bone for Fluffy. And I've made a checklist of other words and terms that might come in handy too.

You'll need some blank paper (a notebook is great), a pen to write with and a stopwatch (or something you can count time with, like a watch). A dictionary might also be useful, should you want to look up the meaning of a word or to get some inspiration.

FAB FIVER!

It started like any other day ...

Once upon a time ...

My name is ...

There was once ...

I didn't want to go ...

Adventure HQ

Checklist:

☐ **An adverb** – tells you how something happens, like quickly or slowly.

☐ **Characters** – the people that exist in books or films.

☐ **Dialogue** – conversations between characters in books or films.

☐ **A metaphor** – describes something as if it was something else. For example, my teacher is a teddy bear.

☐ **Nouns** – naming words that identify a person, place, thing or quality. For example, happiness is an abstract noun.

☐ **Paragraphs** – one or more sentences grouped together that discuss one main subject.

☐ **A simile** – describes something by comparing it to something else, using the words 'like' or 'as'. For example, my teacher is as friendly as a teddy bear.

☐ **A story setting** – the location where a story takes place. This could be anywhere.

☐ **Summary** – a shorter retelling of a longer piece like a book or film, in your own words.

☐ **Synonyms** - different words or phrases that mean the same thing.

Copy that

Your last task before we leave. Copy out the checklist by hand on a blank piece of paper, so you can refer to it as we journey in Creative Writing.

Ocean Corner

After a little while, we reach the shoreline at Ocean Corner. The turquoise water is as still as a pond and very inviting. With snorkels on, we jump in. It's cold! Our skin goes goose bumpy but we soon warm up. We paddle around and see tropical fish and sea creatures of all shapes and sizes. We swim a little farther when all of a sudden we notice a smack of giant jellyfish!

Help Fluffy!

Quick, Fluffy is about to get stung by a venomous jellyfish tendril! To help him swim to safety, write a description of what the giant jellyfish looks like and how big it is.

Hint: check out the 'Fab Fiver' for some useful adjectives.

FAB FIVER!

Bulbous

Slimy

Spineless

Shimmery

Huge

ADVENTURE CLUE:

A 'smack' is a **collective noun**, or a name used to describe a group of something, for jellyfish.

Forest Land

Luckily, your word skills save Fluffy from a nasty sting. We swim towards a shoreline where huge trees are blocking out most of the sky. Welcome to Forest Land. We walk out of the water and quickly dry off in the heat. As we trek deeper into the woods, crinkly leaves brush against us and our feet crunch on a thickening carpet of brambles. At some point we get stuck in the overgrowth.

Amble

Hike

Plod

Ramble

Trudge

Getting untangled

We're trapped in a thicket of massive trees. To break us free, create a new type of tree. What will you name it? What does it look like? What colour is its trunk? And does it have many leaves?

ADVENTURE CLUE:
A **'thicket'** is a dense group of bushes or trees.

13

Punctuation Park

Phew – that was close. We wriggle free and after a short time arrive at a vast manicured lawn. Everything is ordered here, even the birds fly in straight lines overhead. This is Punctuation Park. Looking closer, we see that the garden is actually made up of punctuation. The grass shoots are exclamation marks, the shrub leaves are commas and even the bees are semi-colons.

ADVENTURE CLUE:

A '**semi-colon**' (;) is a punctuation mark that acts like a pause between different parts of a sentence.

A walk in the park

Thankfully, there's no danger here. Although it's useful to understand grammar and punctuation, it's not that important in Creative Writing. So we continue to amble through the park, smelling roses shaped like question marks while Fluffy chases apostrophe butterflies.

ADVENTURE CLUE:

Its and It's

Apostrophes (') represent missing letters when words are shortened, or contracted. *'It's'* either means **it is** or **it has**. For example, **it's** cold (**it is** cold) or **it's** finished (**it has** finished).

Apostrophes can also show possession, that something belongs to someone – like Fluffy**'s** bone. Except in *'its'*, where there is no apostrophe showing possession. So **'its house'** means **the house belonging to it.**

Desert Valley

As we reach the end of the verdant park, the landscape becomes barren and savage. The sun burns fiercely and our feet sink and struggle to tread up and down the sweltering sand dunes of Desert Valley. There is nothing here, just sand stretched as far as the eye can see. We're kept cool by light clothing that covers our heads and bodies; even Fluffy is wearing a sheet. But we're so thirsty ...

ADVENTURE CLUE:

'**Verdant**' means something green with grass or other rich vegetation.

We need water!

We plod on, trying to limit the amount of water we drink. But we soon run out! To save us, write a short paragraph about how you find something to drink. Do you discover a cactus and cut it open? Do we stumble upon an oasis in the middle of the desert? Do you catch a ride from a giant vulture flying overhead who drops you at a supermarket?
It's up to you!

These all are synonyms for the word 'find'.

FAB FIVER!

Locate

Discover

Notice

Uncover

Reveal

Animal Kingdom

You did it! Fully quenched, we power on to make it out of the desert. The terrain is flatter here but more jungle-like. We start to hear distant roars and birdsong and can feel the vibrations of movement in Animal Kingdom. For safety, we keep Fluffy on a leash as we trudge past creeping spiders, slithering snakes, galloping zebras, lumbering elephants, laughing hyenas, rough and wrinkly rhinos, powerful lions and many unusual creatures.

If we could talk to the animals ...

At a forest opening we discover a new species of animal: the pandrab, a cross between a panda and a rabbit. *"Flurp, flummer mufffhg reff Leslie duh"*, she says. Somehow we understand this as: *"Hello, my name is Leslie."* Introduce yourself to the friendly pandrab, writing down your conversation and anything else Leslie says in response.

ADVENTURE CLUE:

Ending verbs with –*ing* (or the **present participle**) is a great way of describing an animal's movements or actions.

These are alternative words for says; said.

FAB FIVER!

Remarks; remarked

Replies; replied

Answers; answered

Comments; commented

Notes; noted

19

Candy Land

You make such a great first impression, that Leslie tells us about a shortcut out of the kingdom. We turn left, weave right, all hop on one foot (even Fluffy!) to avoid some quicksand before arriving at the gigantic lollipop walls of Candy Land. Walking through red liquorice gates we are hit by the smell of bubblegum. We pass houses made of gingerbread, candy cane trees and a river of lemonade.

FAB FIVER!

These are all synonyms for 'big'. Perhaps look in a **dictionary** or **thesaurus** if you want to discover other similar words.

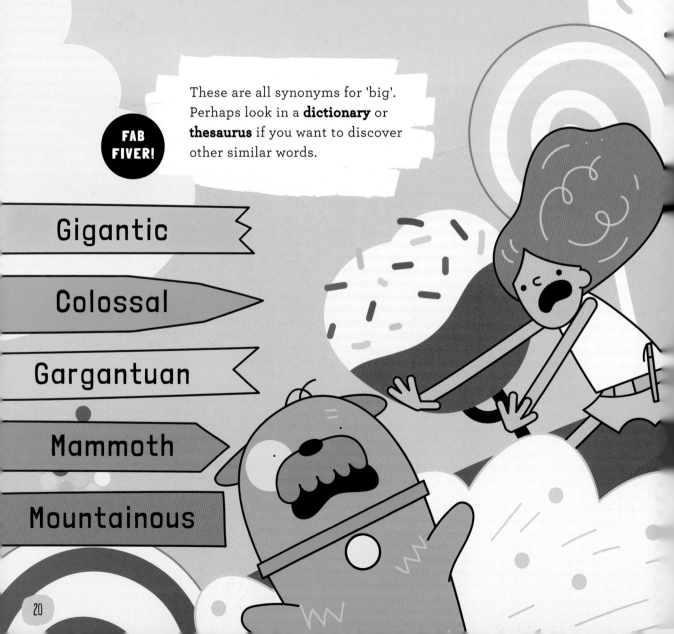

Gigantic

Colossal

Gargantuan

Mammoth

Mountainous

Don't eat anything!

Fluffy runs off his leash towards a bank of cotton candy bushes. He starts to eat the pink cloud-like sweets. Oh! No! He's suddenly transformed into an ice cream. To help Fluffy turn back into a dog, imagine and write down what it feels like to be turned into an ice-cream cone. What do you look like? Do you feel cold? Are you a particular flavour? Can you move around at all?

ADVENTURE CLUE:

A useful way of imagining yourself as something or someone else, is to close your eyes and try to picture it in your mind.

Spectral Spookyville

Fluffy licks your face to thank you for saving him. We move quickly, avoiding any temptation to eat the sweets. After a while, we approach some creepy gates with 'Spectral Spookyville' written in cast iron. It's night-time here and eerily silent. We feel scared as we amble through a veil of thick fog, passing deserted houses and tombstones and terrifying trees that seem to be watching us. We hear screams ...

ADVENTURE CLUE:

'Spectral' is an **adjective**, that describes something being or seeming like a ghost.

These are all useful words and phrases to express an amount of time having passed.

How many monsters?

Aaargh – we turn in the direction of noise and see a phantom floating towards us! We start to run, only to trip over a zombie and a ghoul hiding in the fog. Help us get away. Using your **stopwatch** to count – write down the names of as many different types of monster as you can remember (or make up) in **60 seconds**.

Before long

After a little while

Eventually

Later on

After some time

Outer Space

You really know your monsters. We make it safely out of Spookyville and eventually reach a strange platform that looks like a mammoth metallic mushroom. Out of curiosity, we all step up onto it. *Whoosh* – we're instantly beamed onto an empty spaceship in Outer Space. There's zero gravity, so we're floating and spinning around. Out of tiny windows we see a blanket of twinkling stars and a purple planet glowing in the distance.

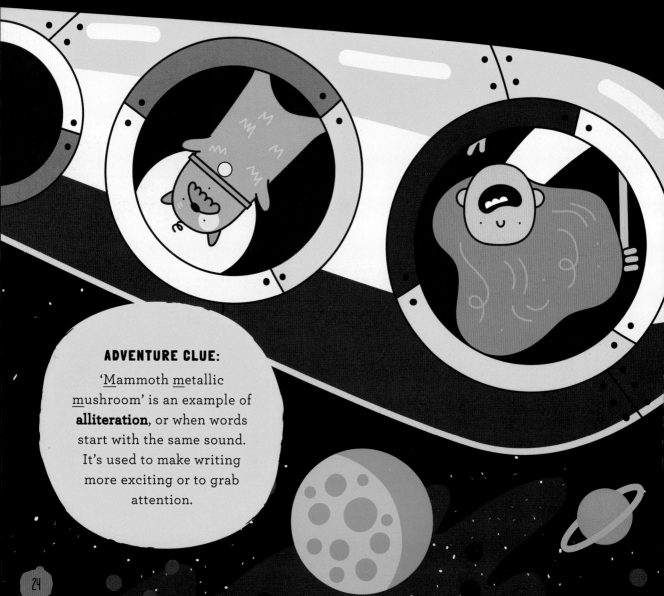

ADVENTURE CLUE:
'Mammoth metallic mushroom' is an example of **alliteration**, or when words start with the same sound. It's used to make writing more exciting or to grab attention.

Down to earth

Fluffy sees a big red button and pushes it with his left paw. *Kablam* – we all fall to the floor. With gravity back on, we start to look around the ship for ways to escape. What happens next? Write a short paragraph, imagining how we get back down to earth. You'll need to include at least one use of alliteration, in order for your creative solution to work.

FAB FIVER!

Space or science fiction stories might include some of these words.

Teleport

Portal

Alien

Force-field

Starship

Volcania

We're back on solid ground – but somewhere new. A huge volcano looms, spewing lava and chunks of molten rock as big as cars. This must be Volcania. We're hungry, so we stop for a quick snack and use our maps to plot a course around the volcano. We set off again but soon the sky darkens, as the wind picks up strength and a funnel forms in the clouds ahead. It's a tornado!

These **nouns** are all examples of extreme weather events or conditions.

FAB FIVER!

Blizzard

Heatwave

Drought

Avalanche

Flood

Land of natural disasters

Fluffy whimpers and hides between our legs. Panicked, our first instinct is to run but there's no way to know where the tornado will head. So we huddle together for safety. Suddenly the ground shakes violently. There's an earthquake too! Quick, help change this dire situation by imagining a lovely summer's day. Write about all the fun things you do, describing the perfect weather.

ADVENTURE CLUE:

An 'instinct' is a natural or automatic way of acting or thinking.

Poetry Place

The ground is still
The wind is calm
We pick up pace

We climb mountains
Cross rivers
To Poetry Place

A world of music,
Words rhyming
Or falling apart

Where stories
And ideas are
Made into art.

ADVENTURE CLUE:

A free verse poem doesn't have
to rhyme or use a structure like
other poems.

Be a poet

Some poems read quickly, while others go slow
Some even tell tales of times long ago

Many are structured in verses and keep to a rhyme
While others do
Whatever
They
Want.

It's lovely to be here
But more adventure awaits
Please write us a poem
So we can escape.

FLUFFY'S ACROSTIC:

Furry

Licks

Unyielding;

Fierce

Friend

Yapping

ADVENTURE CLUE:

An **acrostic poem** is a poem where certain letters, usually the first letters of each line, are used to spell out a word or phrase.

The Robot Ruins

Thanks to your poem, we continue on our journey. The scenery changes from lush grasslands to an arid, rocky expanse. We enter what looks like an abandoned scrapyard. At the centre lies a massive pile of steel, glass and wire coils. This is Robot Ruins. As we get closer to the mound, we start to hear a whirring noise. "What are you doing here?!", says a shrill and angry voice at great volume.

Heap

Stack

Mound

Mass

Rickle

FAB FIVER! These are synonyms for the word 'pile'.

Dream machine

We look around but can't see where the voice is coming from. Suddenly, the mound of metal begins to move and two red disc eyes light up – staring right at us. The robot pile is alive! Time to go. Help us escape by creating your own robot. What can it do? Give it a name and write a description of what it looks like.

These are all synonyms for 'robot'. You can add more variety to your robot stories by using a combination of these words.

FAB FIVER!

Machine

Automaton

Bot

Android

Droid

Speak Street

"*That was a close call*", remarks Ms. Adjective.

"*Woof, woof!*" replies Fluffy.

"*We've been walking for ages. Where are we now?*" you ask grumpily.

"*This is Speak Street*", she says. "*It's a land of dialogue and talking*"

"*But what's so important about that?*" you interrupt.

"*Well, Creative Writing has all sorts of words. Some written down, some spoken aloud or sung. And some that show what characters are thinking or feeling, verbally.*"

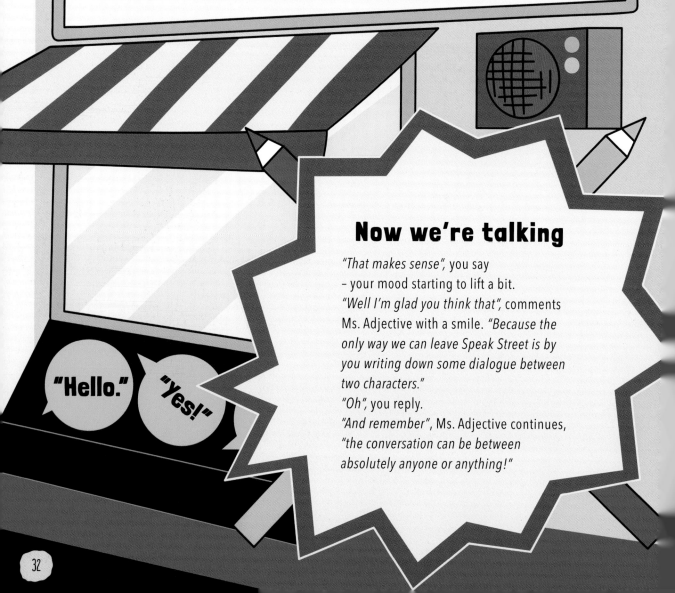

"Hello."

"Yes!"

Now we're talking

"That makes sense", you say
– your mood starting to lift a bit.
"Well I'm glad you think that", comments Ms. Adjective with a smile. *"Because the only way we can leave Speak Street is by you writing down some dialogue between two characters."*
"Oh", you reply.
"And remember", Ms. Adjective continues, *"the conversation can be between absolutely anyone or anything!"*

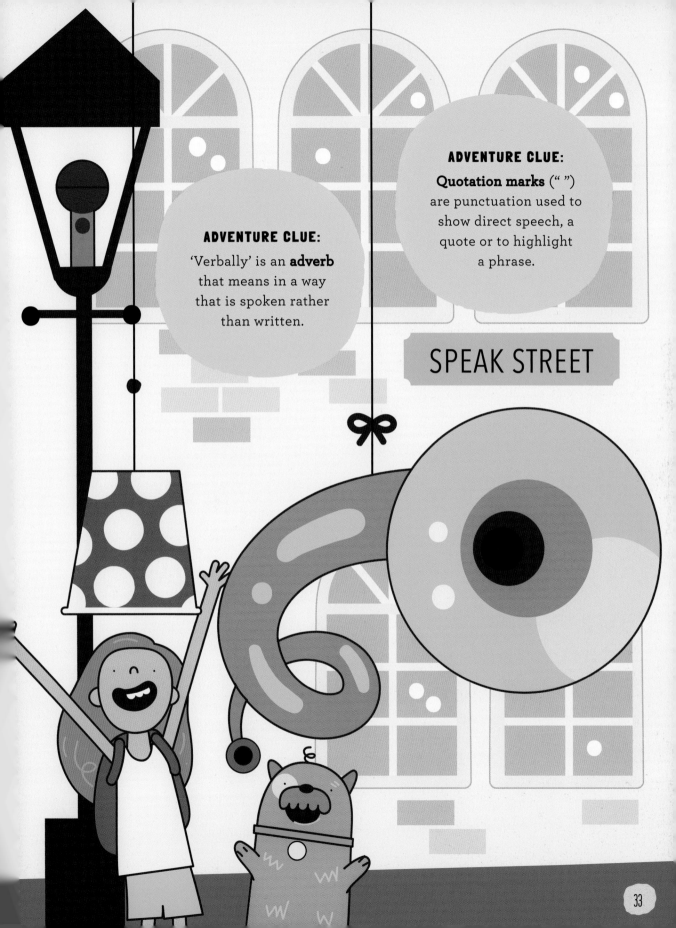

ADVENTURE CLUE:

'Verbally' is an **adverb** that means in a way that is spoken rather than written.

ADVENTURE CLUE:

Quotation marks (" ") are punctuation used to show direct speech, a quote or to highlight a phrase.

SPEAK STREET

Mega Metropolis

We see an outline on the horizon, with towers higher than the clouds. Welcome to Mega Metropolis. As we enter the city limits, we're bombarded with the sound of activity: cars and buses speeding down avenues; crowds of people walking and talking along its streets; a furious pace of life. Everyone lives in skyscrapers here. Pedestrians push past us in a hurry, as we make our way towards the city centre.

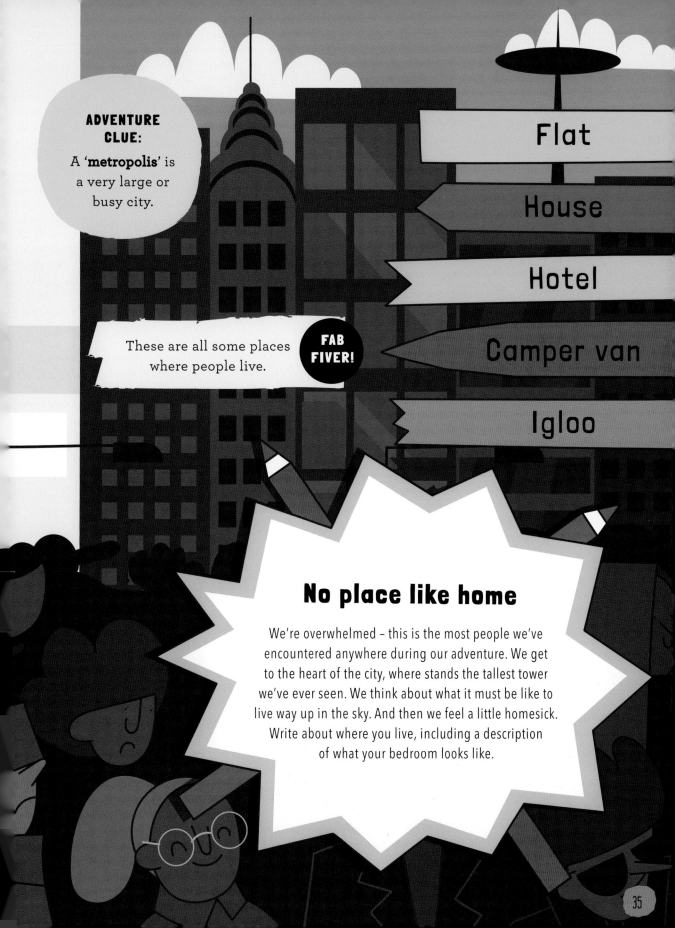

ADVENTURE CLUE:

A '**metropolis**' is a very large or busy city.

Flat

House

Hotel

Camper van

Igloo

These are all some places where people live.

FAB FIVER!

No place like home

We're overwhelmed – this is the most people we've encountered anywhere during our adventure. We get to the heart of the city, where stands the tallest tower we've ever seen. We think about what it must be like to live way up in the sky. And then we feel a little homesick. Write about where you live, including a description of what your bedroom looks like.

Island of Disappearing Words

By imagining your home, we're able to get out of the city. Before long, we arrive at a riverbank. There's an empty boat and we can see a small island across the calm blue water. We row towards it. As we reach the shoreline and disembark, something strange begins to happen. With every step ... take, we see a part ... the island dis–... The trees ... ... blank and the ground ... Without words ... is nothing.

Paddle

Sail

Punt

Take the oars

Propel

The blanks

We're ... danger.
We must ... back ... the boat.
Help ...! Finish ... story by fill-... the blanks.

One day a ___ girl was ___ to the park.
She felt ___ because ___ her ___ gave her
a ___scarf. The weather was ___ and she ___
her scarf ___ around her ___.

She ___ and ___ on the rocket-shaped
climbing frame and the ___ before it was
time to go home. She now felt ___ so she ___
her coat and ___ home.

... CLUE:

Ellipsis (...) is
punctuation made up
of three dots that shows
when a word or sentence
is missing from a piece
of writing.

37

Favourite Food Mountain

You did it again! Our words return and we journey on. We walk until we feel tired and our stomachs start growling like hungry bears. We're about to stop to eat from our dwindling provisions, when we suddenly spot a small mountain in the near distance. We check our maps and get excited when we realise it's Favourite Food Mountain – a magical place where all the best foods you can imagine become real.

ADVENTURE CLUE:

'**Dwindling**' is an adjective that describes something becoming less in number, or smaller.

These are all words that describe something that tastes delicious.

Mouth-watering

Delectable

Flavourful

Scrumptious

Finger-licking

Yummy things to eat!

There's the delicious smell of all our favourite things in the air. The mountain is made up of bones and broccoli, hamburgers and chicken legs, watermelon and orange juice, chocolate bars and cucumber sandwiches, samosas and so much more. But only you can help us get to eat any of it, by imagining your best meal ever and writing it down.

Likeness Lake

With stuffed backpacks and full stomachs, we move like snails. The land is rocky and our exhausted legs wobble like jelly. After what seems like ten years, we arrive at Likeness Lake. The lake is a giant puddle glistening in the sunlight, as inviting as a big hug. We decide to go for a swim. The water is as cold as ice but we find this refreshing. We happily float together like otters.

Stop floating

Darkness falls like a curtain but we're blind to it. We continue floating like driftwood, not realising that we're trapped in the muddier waters of simile and metaphor – lost in so many descriptions! Help us leave Likeness Lake. Write an explanation of how we get out of the water, using only one simile and one metaphor in your account.

FAB FIVER!

These are alternative words for 'land'.

Terrain

Ground

Countryside

Landscape

Topography

ADVENTURE CLUE:
'Glistening' is an **adjective** that means shining with a sparkling light.

The Switch Stone

It's daytime again. Fluffy shakes his fur dry and we start to walk. We look at our maps and can see that we're headed for 'The Switch Stone'. After some time, we approach what looks like a grey egg the size of an elephant. It's a wondrous thing to see. But before we can warn each other about not getting too close, Fluffy excitedly runs up to it and has a sniff.

Who are you now?

As his nose lightly skims against the stone, we hear a loud clap. Instantly, Ms. Adjective gets on all fours and starts barking and Fluffy stands on his hind legs and shouts: "What have you done now?" They've switched bodies! To help them swap back, write a paragraph from Ms. Adjective's perspective (pretending to be her) – imagining your first impressions of being a dog and what it feels like.

ADVENTURE CLUE:

'**Wondrous**' is something that inspires a feeling of wonder or delight.

ADVENTURE CLUE:

'**Perspective**' is someone's outlook or point of view, which is usually based on their experiences and personality.

Story Summit

Back in our correct bodies, we move on. Looking at our maps, we can see that we're almost at the end of our adventure in The World of Creative Writing. It feels like we've been away for ages. As we trudge the grainy soil of this final land, we notice the topography change and get steeper. We soon realise that we're actually climbing a mountain, headed towards Story Summit.

ADVENTURE CLUE:

A story is very much like climbing a mountain. In the **beginning**, you introduce your main characters. In the **middle**, they face various twists and obstacles going up the mountain until they reach the summit, or climax – their greatest challenge. And in the **end**, after the biggest problem is solved, they make their way back down again.

What's the story?

We ascend the snake-like trail, passing all sorts of things you wouldn't expect to find up a mountain including giant jellyfish, zombies, pandrabs and a massive robot head. We reach the summit and looking over the edge, we now see that the mountain is made up of all the elements of our journey. In order to get us home, write a summary in <u>three</u> paragraphs of your favourite parts of our adventure.

These are synonyms for 'summit'.

FAB FIVER!

Mountaintop

Peak

Crest

Apex

Crown

Still at Story Summit

That was a great effort, but we're still stuck on the mountaintop! We hear strange noises below, so we move to the edge of the peak to investigate. We're a little unnerved when we see things scrambling and moving down there. A cotton candy bush floats into view, followed by a giant jellyfish, a spaceship and The Switch Stone.

All about Fluffy

At first, we don't understand why we're seeing these specific things. But then we realise: they all relate to Fluffy and his experiences in Creative Writing. So, the only way to get home must be to tell Fluffy's story. Imagine you're Fluffy. Write down <u>three</u> paragraphs from his perspective, describing his favourite parts of our adventure.

Back home

Well done! Your brilliant creativity and imagination has triumphed in The World of Creative Writing.

Story Summit suddenly transforms into Adventure HQ, where we're greeted by Meow, Scaredy and Squawk. You say goodbye to everyone, giving Ms. Adjective and Fluffy an extra-long hug. Then you close your eyes. And when you open them, you're here. You were home all along.

"Come back any time!"

The End.